D0319732

DreamWorks
DRAGONS
ULTIMATE
MOVIE GUIDE

Special thanks to Sara Stanford
Design by 38a The Shop

HODDER CHILDREN'S BOOKS

First published in Great Britain in 2019 by Hodder and Stoughton

1 3 5 7 9 10 8 6 4 2

A CIP catalogue record for this book
is available from the British Library.

ISBN: 978 1 444 94693 2

Printed and bound in China

The paper and board used in this book are made from wood from responsible sources

Hodder Children's Books
An imprint of
Hachette Children's Group
Part of Hodder and Stoughton
Carmelite House
50 Victoria Embankment
London, EC4Y 0DZ

An Hachette UK Company
www.hachette.co.uk

www.hachettechildrens.co.uk

DreamWorks

DRAGONS

ULTIMATE

MOVIE GUIDE

WELCOME TO BERK!

Inside this Ultimate Guide you'll get to hang out with all your favourite Berkians and dragons, as well as experience the highs and lows of Viking life on Berk.

Astrid

Fishlegs

For generations, if you lived on Berk, you learned to slay dragons – your life depended on it! Dragon training was an everyday part of Viking life and began early.

It all started a very long time ago with a Viking named Bork the Very, Very Unfortunate. He lived on Berk and his life was made difficult by the dragons he shared the island with. They'd creep up on him and steal his food, ruin his crops or even burn down his hut!

So Bork created The Book of Dragons to pass down to future generations of Vikings so that they would know exactly what type of creatures they were dealing with. Over the years, the Vikings added to the book and grew to hate all dragons!

Hiccup
Snotlout
Ruffnut
Tuffnut
The Vikings when we first met them!

LIFE ON BERK

If you dare to duel with the wildest, most dangerous creatures on earth, then Berk is the place for you.

Life on Berk is pretty tough if you're not a natural when it comes to dragon killing. You've got to be bold and ruthless to survive life on this island and Hiccup is neither!

The way of life is made even more difficult due to the extreme weather on the island. It is almost always cold and dark with plenty of hail or snow.

Besides the wild weather, Berk also has a much more serious problem ... dragons! The dragons steal the Vikings' food and constantly destroy the village. Every time the Vikings rebuild, the dragons come back and destroy it all over again!

You can't call yourself a true Viking until you've killed a dragon, but one young boy is about to change everything ...

DreamWorks

HOW TO TRAIN YOUR DRAGON

A young Viking named Hiccup has spent his whole life trying to prove himself to his father, Stoick the Vast. Stoick is the Viking Chief of Berk and is the toughest Viking of them all!

Hiccup is desperate to follow in his father's footsteps and be a powerful leader and infamous dragon killer. The only problem is Hiccup isn't as strong as most other Vikings. He struggles to pick up the weapons let alone use them!

But everything begins to change for Hiccup when he shoots down a Night Fury dragon using a special homemade Mangler weapon. Night Furies are incredibly rare and the most deadly of all dragons. Very little is known about them and no one has ever seen one in real life.

Hiccup can't wait to prove he is a true Viking to his father by killing the Night Fury. But when Hiccup approaches the injured Night Fury he sees the fear in the creature's eyes and can't bring himself to kill it.

Meanwhile, Stoick's friend Gobber persuades him to let Hiccup join dragon training. When Hiccup finds out, he knows he'll never be able to keep up! The first day of training is even worse than Hiccup imagined. The other kids his age make fun of him and he just can't get anything right.

Hiccup begins spending time with the Night Fury and he nicknames him Toothless. In fact, whenever Hiccup isn't at dragon training, he's hanging out with Toothless.

By watching Toothless, Hiccup realises that everyone has misjudged the dragons and that they're only defending themselves. Slowly, Hiccup gains Toothless' trust and they learn how to communicate.

Through his friendship with Toothless, Hiccup learns how to control the dragons and uses his new skills in dragon training. The other trainees can't believe their eyes. How has Hiccup become a dragon master?

Suddenly all the trainees want to be Hiccup's friend. A girl called Astrid notices that Hiccup is always sneaking away after class and knows he's up to something.

Hiccup's success at dragon training means he wins the 'prize' of killing a dragon in front of the entire village. Horrified by the idea, Hiccup decides to run away with Toothless ... and fast.

Astrid follows Hiccup after dragon training and discovers his big secret – Toothless! Hiccup has a lot of explaining to do.

Hiccup wants to show Astrid how great Toothless really is, so he takes her for a ride. While the three of them are flying they discover an enormous dragon's nest guarded by a gigantic dragon called the Red Death!

Toothless returns them safely to Berk and Hiccup asks Astrid to promise not to tell the other Vikings about the dragon's nest. He knows that it would only lead to trouble. Together, Astrid and Hiccup make it their mission to change the way that Vikings see dragons.

At the dragon killing ceremony, Hiccup drops his weapons to prove that dragons are not dangerous. The other Vikings attack the dragon thinking they're saving Hiccup but it only causes the dragon to become angry.

Toothless, hearing Hiccup is in trouble, flies to help him but is captured by Stoick and chained up. To make matters worse, Hiccup accidently reveals the location of the dragon's nest!

Determined to end the war with the dragons once and for all, Stoick quickly loads Toothless onto his ship and together with the rest of the Vikings, sets sail to find the nest.

Hiccup knows he must do something. He persuades Astrid and the rest of the Vikings-in-training to fly the dragons! They quickly race after the Viking fleet.

Meanwhile, Stoick finds the dragon's nest and fires catapults to bring out the dragons. When the dragons fly out of the nest without a fight, Stoick realises his mistake. But it's too late!

The Red Death appears and Stoick and Gobber try to distract it so the other Vikings can escape. But before long all their ships are on fire! Hiccup and his friends arrive and spot Toothless chained up on a burning ship.

With help from Stoick, Hiccup frees Toothless. Hiccup and Toothless fly together to take on the Red Death.

Luring the dragon high up into the sky, Toothless blasts the dragon just as it is about to breath fire, causing it to explode! Hiccup is thrown from Toothless and they both fall into the flames.

Stoick runs to see Toothless lying on the ground with no sign of Hiccup. Everyone is devastated but then, Toothless opens his wing to reveal Hiccup next to him. Hiccup is alive but lost part of his leg in the battle.

Stoick cannot thank Toothless enough for protecting his son and he has never been more proud to call himself Hiccup's father. What's more, Hiccup's bravery has ended the feud between dragons and Vikings – they can now live in peace!

HICCUP AND TOOTHLESS

Let's get to know Hiccup and the Night Fury, Toothless!

- Hiccup hasn't always fitted in with the other Vikings - he'd never killed a dragon and he's so small he couldn't even pick up the weapons! But Hiccup makes up for his size with tactical thinking and knowledge of dragons.

- Hiccup loves to draw and he's never without his journal and a pencil. This talent helps him on his adventures as he can sketch maps, draw dragons and note down important information.

Hiccup is assistant to the village blacksmith, Gobber. This means he's got serious skills when it comes to building weapons, like his bola-flinging Mangler.

"Other places have ponies or parrots, we have dragons!"

Hiccup is always designing new contraptions. He made a leather saddle and tail fin for Toothless. It may have taken a few tries to get it right but he never gave up!

- Toothless lost part of his tail when he fell from the sky. The new tail fin Hiccup builds means they can fly together. Hiccup controls the tail fin from his saddle.

Did you know?

Hiccup is left-handed.

CLASS: Strike

WINGSPAN: 45 feet

HABITAT: Unknown

SKILLS: Dive bombing, ability to camouflage itself in the night sky

Did you know?

A Night Fury has a row of fins down its spine that can split in two to help them fly even faster!

- Toothless is a Night Fury. They are the fastest and rarest dragon species.

- Night Fury's can fly faster than the speed of sound - that's more than 750 miles per hour!

- Night Fury's can dive-bomb and shoot plasma blasts at their enemies with frightening accuracy.

- Toothless' plasma blasts explode and incinerate anything that gets in his way.

- Night Furies are invisible in the night sky and seem to appear out of nowhere!

- Night Fury's have amazing vision in the dark so are just as dangerous during attacks at night.

- Toothless is the only known Night Fury.

- Toothless and Hiccup form a very strong bond. It's this friendship that brings the Vikings and dragons together.

ASTRID

Strong, loyal and hardworking, Astrid is the kind of friend you want on your side! She's fiercely competitive and will stop at nothing to protect those she cares about.

- Astrid may be petite but she makes up for it with her agility.

- Astrid is in dragon training with Hiccup. She wants to be number one and isn't impressed with Hiccup's dragon taming 'skills'.

Unlike the rest of the Vikings, Astrid doesn't wear a helmet in combat - she wears a headband.

- Nothing gets past Astrid! She knows that Hiccup is up to something when he begins acing every task at dragon training. Before long, Astrid is in on his secret and she's just as determined to protect Toothless.

FISHLEGS

If it's dragon facts you want, Fishlegs is your Viking!
He's a walking, talking dragon dictionary.

Although he likes to seem tough, Fishlegs is more scared than Hiccup during dragon training!

- Fishlegs is kind and caring. He becomes a good friend to Hiccup.

- Fishlegs dresses head to toe in fur. Perfect for freezing Berk winters!

- Fishlegs knows everything about dragons. He can't believe his eyes when he gets to meet a Night Fury!

- Fishlegs' knowledge comes in handy when the friends are faced with the Red Death. Only Fishlegs can remember her weakness!

STOICK THE VAST

Stoick is Viking Chief on Berk – he also happens to be Hiccup's father!

- Stoick is brave, strong and well respected on Berk. Everyone is also a little afraid of him – including Hiccup!

- Stoick and Hiccup couldn't look more different. Sometimes he can't believe Hiccup is his son.

- Stoick enrolls Hiccup in dragon training and won't take no for an answer. He longs for his son to be a strong and mighty Viking but Hiccup isn't your average Viking. He's scrawny and sensitive – two things Stoick has zero patience for!

Before sending Hiccup to dragon training, Stoick gives him a helmet made from Hiccup's mother's armour.

GOBBER

Gobber is now Berk's resident blacksmith and dragon dentist!

- Gobber is in charge of dragon training. He teaches the young Vikings dragon-battling skills and the best way to catch dragons.

- Gobber is great friends with Stoick and it was Gobber's idea to send Hiccup to dragon training.

Gobber fought alongside Stoick in the Dragons Wars and lost his arm while fighting a dragon. Now he replaces his missing arm with different tools depending on the job he's working on!

- Gobber provides Berk with the strongest armour and weapons for fighting dragons. Hiccup is Gobber's hardworking and inventive assistant.

Did you know?

Gobber lost his arm and leg while battling a Monstrous Nightmare – the same type of dragon as Hookfang.

RUFFNUT AND TUFFNUT

These troublesome twins are always arguing but they're never far from one another's side!

- The twins are extremely competitive and love to out-do one another at any opportunity.

- Ruffnut is a typical Viking. She's a tough, all-action girl who is well known for being sarcastic. Her weapon of choice is a spear.

- Ruffnut likes to talk ... a lot. The other Vikings don't always appreciate her constant commentary though!

During the final battle Ruffnut and Tuffnut share a Hideous Zippleback they call Barf and Belch. They have trouble riding their dragon because they can never agree on anything and to make things worse, Barf and Belch sometimes argue, too!

- Tuffnut's weapon of choice is an iron mace. He loves it so much he calls it Macey and even speaks to it!

- Despite not always getting along, the twins can always rely on each other if they are in danger.

- The twins love to pretend - a skill that often comes in handy when dealing with unfriendly strangers!

Did you know?

Ruffnut and Tuffnut's surname is Thorston.

Ruffnut and Tuffnut love nothing more than playing pranks! They always have a new trick up their sleeve and particularly enjoy scaring Fishlegs.

SNOTLOUT

This Dragon Rider is the smartest, most popular and highly skilled Viking-in-training ... or so he says!

- Snotlout is so strong he's been known to lift sheep over his head with ease.

When faced with danger, Snotlout has bags of energy and stamina.

- Snotlout thinks he's the most beautiful and popular Viking in town. One thing Snotlout doesn't have much of is modesty ...

- Snotlout's weapon of choice is a simple hammer. He doesn't need a fancy weapon when he has all the skill!

- No one has to wait too long to hear all about Snotlout and his strengths. He would talk about himself all day given the chance!

THE RED DEATH

The Red Death is a gigantic dragon that commands other dragons to raid villages and bring her food.

SPECIES: Stoker Class

SIZE: 999 feet

WINGSPAN: 320 feet

HABITAT: Volcanoes

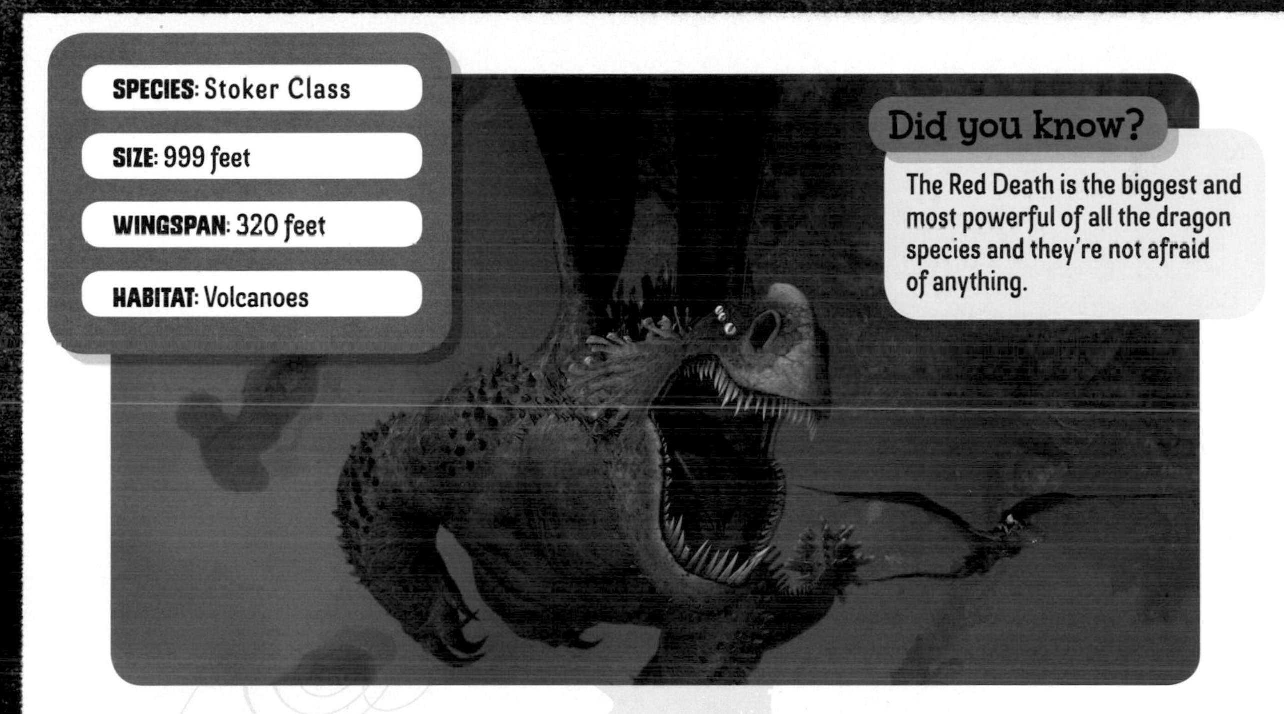

Did you know?

The Red Death is the biggest and most powerful of all the dragon species and they're not afraid of anything.

- Hiccup, Astrid and Toothless first discover the Red Death when they fly into the dragon's nest. She comes out of hiding to snap up a Gronckle!

- The Red Death doesn't hunt itself - it sends other dragons to do the work for them. If the dragon doesn't bring back enough food, the Red Death will eat it instead!

- The Red Death has six eyes, its tail is covered in deadly spikes and it has vicious claws and razor-sharp fangs.

- Red Death flame jets are so powerful that they take out an entire fleet of Viking ships!

- Unlike most other dragons, the Red Death cannot be tamed.

GRONCKLE AND MONSTROUS NIGHTMARE

- Gronckles are lava-spewing dragons with fast-moving wings but are well known for being lazy. They have even been known to fall asleep mid-flight!

- Gronckles can fly backwards and if they hold their breath, the bumps on their body fire off in every direction.

- Fishlegs teams up with a Gronckle and names it Meatlug!

SPECIES: Gronckle

CLASS: Boulder

SIZE: 14 feet

WINGSPAN: 18 feet

HABITAT: Forests and caves

SKILLS: Flying backwards, hovering and dropping in the air

SPECIES: Monstrous Nightmare

CLASS: Stoker

SIZE: 61 feet

WINGSPAN: 68 feet

HABITAT: Forests

SKILLS: Fire burst, wing blast, jaw expansion

- Monstrous Nightmare dragons are aggressive, powerful and fiery. They can set themselves on fire as a form of defence.

- Snotlout teams up with this Monstrous Nightmare, naming it Hookfang. Of course he would choose a particularly dangerous dragon!

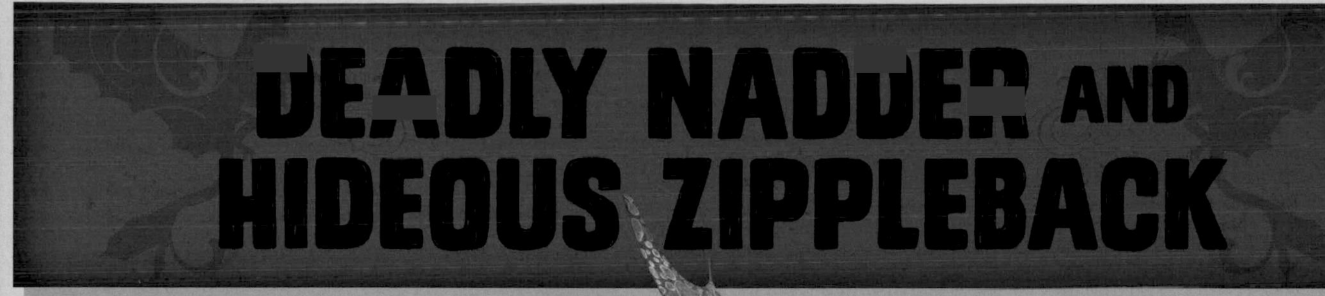

DEADLY NADDER AND HIDEOUS ZIPPLEBACK

- Deadly Nadders are tracker dragons so have a very strong and accurate sense of smell.
- The magnesium fire from a Deadly Nadder is the hottest of all dragons!
- Astrid and Stromfly make the perfect team. They have power, strength and intelligence!

SPECIES: Deadly Nadder

CLASS: Tracker

SIZE: 30 feet

WINGSPAN: 42 feet

SKILLS: Poisonous spikes

- One head emits gas while the other creates a spark setting off an explosion.
- Not only is the gas from a Hideous Zippleback toxic, it's also thick enough to hide in.
- Hideous Zipplebacks have twin heads - no wonder it's the dragon that Tuffnut and Ruffnut choose!

SPECIES: Hideous Zippleback

CLASS: Mystery

SIZE: 66 feet

WINGSPAN: 38 feet

HABITAT: Caverns and forests

SKILLS: Connecting heads and tails to make a flaming wheel of death!

DRAGONS, DRAGONS AND MORE DRAGONS

Here's a selection of more fearsome dragons that can be found on Berk.

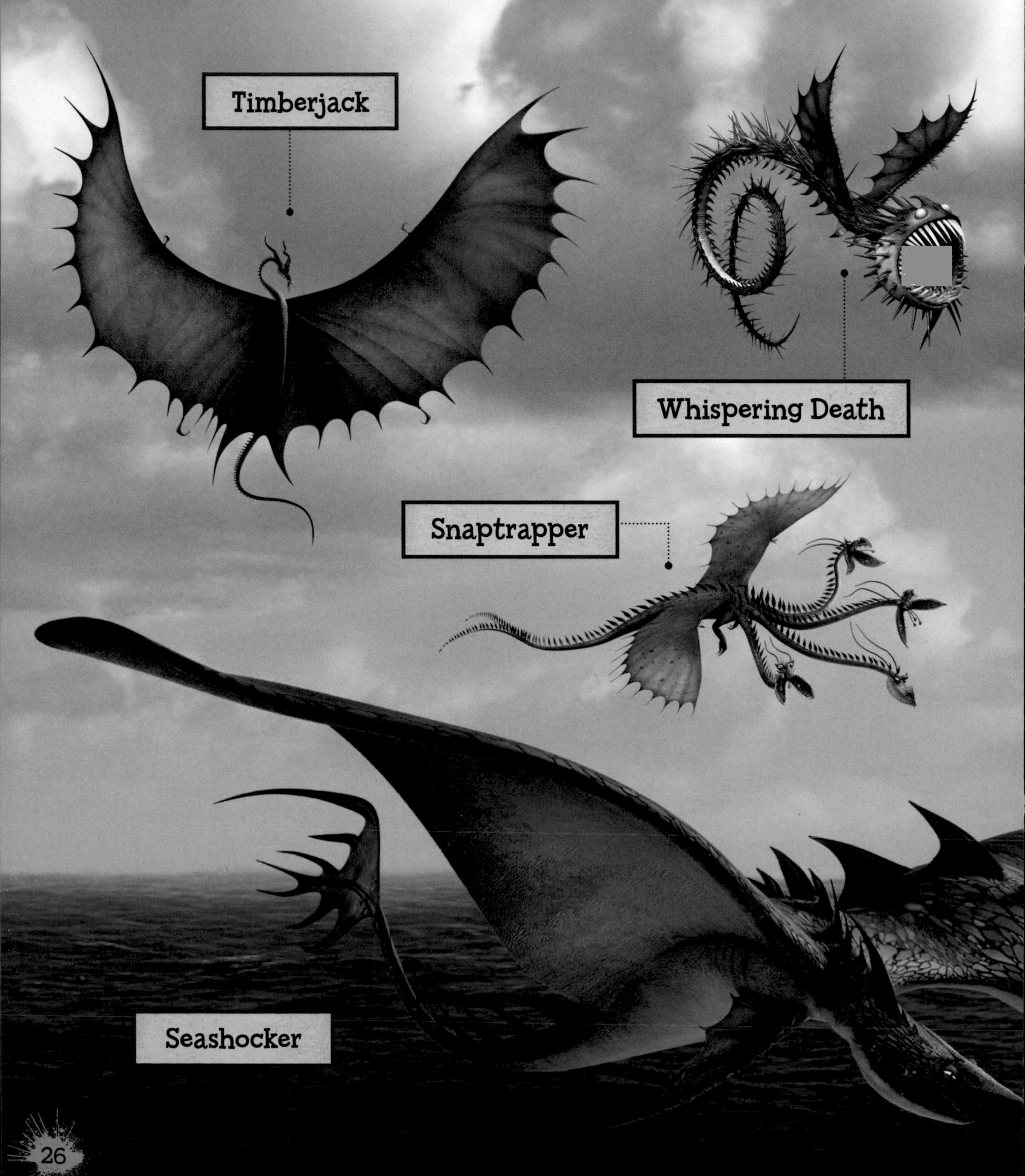

Terrible Terror
Thunderdrum
Stormcutter

ALL ABOUT BERK!

Berk has been home to Vikings like Hiccup and Stoick for generations.

The island of Berk is very varied. It has forests, caves, waterfalls and beaches, as well as the village.

Berk isn't known for its welcoming weather - it snows for nine months of the year and you can expect hail for the remaining three!

Dragons and Vikings have always battled to survive on Berk. Before Hiccup met Toothless, dragon raids were common and the village was often destroyed by fires.

Any food that grows here is tough and tasteless and the people that grow here are even more so!

ALL AT SEA

The Vikings of Berk travel the sea in their specially crafted longships.

Longships are the transport of choice for the Vikings of Berk. These hardy ships can travel long distances and carry many Vikings.

The sail is decorated with a dragon design and the ship has a fierce dragon carved into the front. They are designed to scare away enemies and show their power over the dragons.

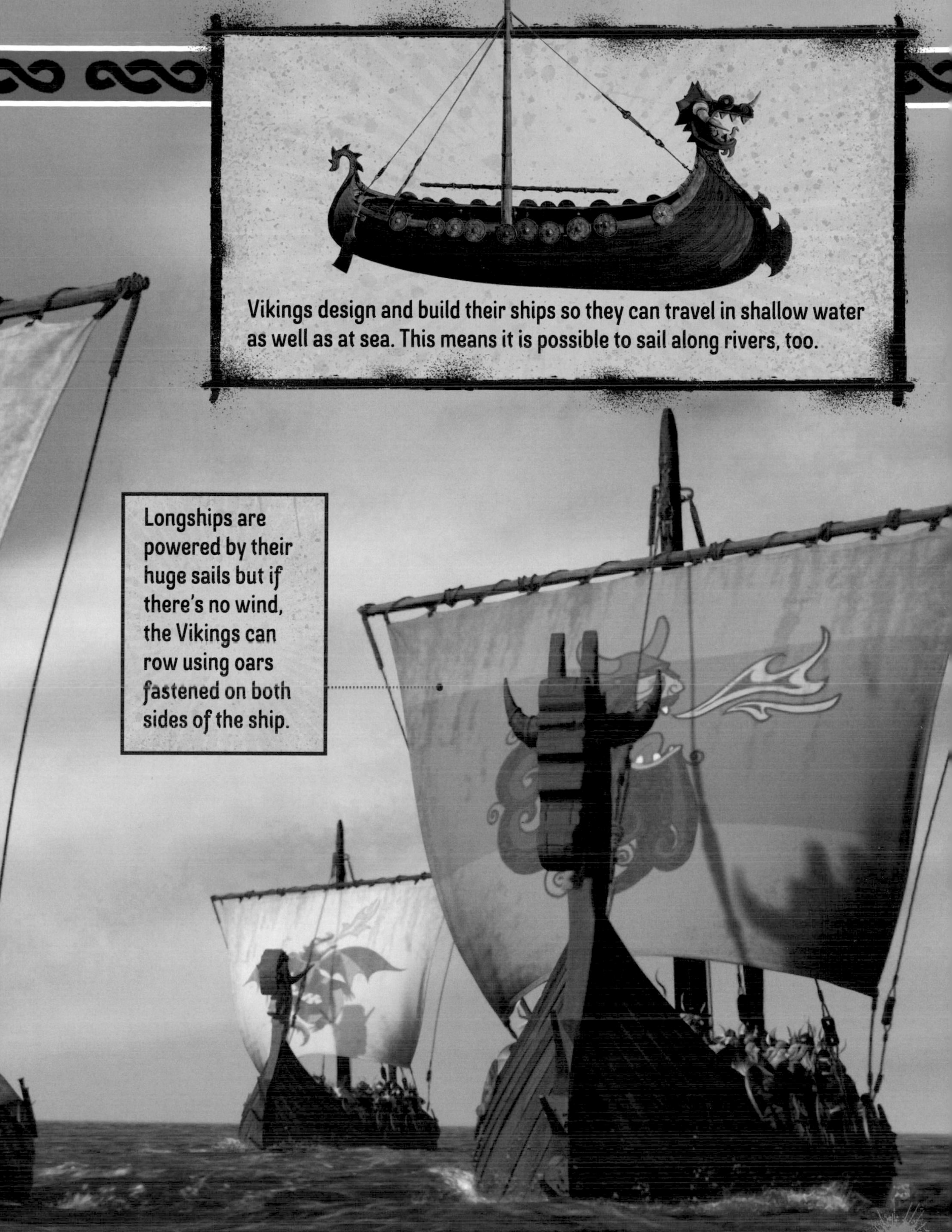

Vikings design and build their ships so they can travel in shallow water as well as at sea. This means it is possible to sail along rivers, too.

Longships are powered by their huge sails but if there's no wind, the Vikings can row using oars fastened on both sides of the ship.

VIKING PROTECTION

When you're a Viking, protecting yourself comes first.

The most important piece of equipment for Vikings are their shields. It's more important than any type of weapon. They need all the protection they can get when they're facing fire-breathing dragons!

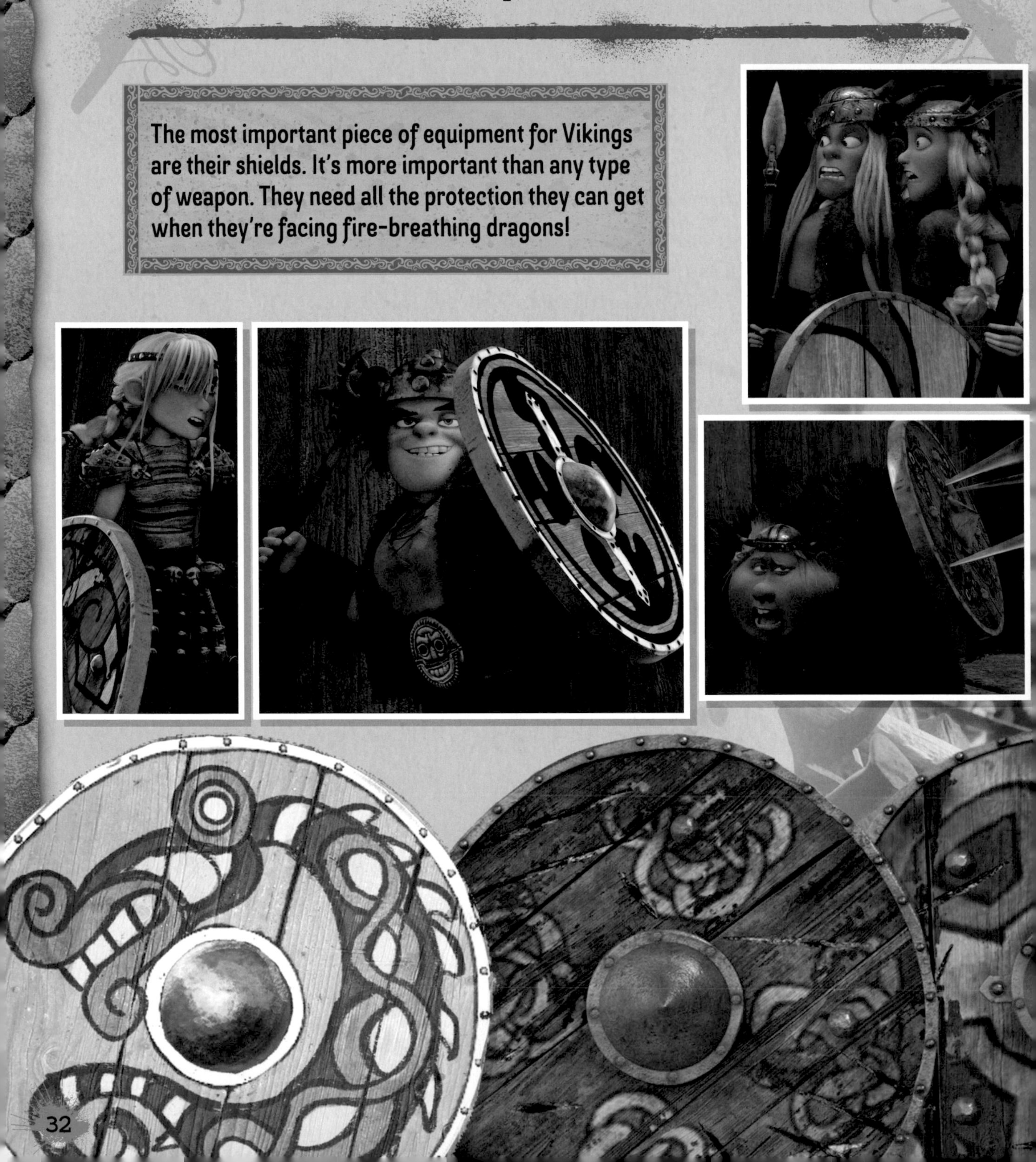

When faced with Red Death, even their Viking shields aren't enough to protect them!

Did you know?

Hiccup throws his helmet and shield to the floor when he faces a Monstrous Nightmare. He wants to prove he's not like other Vikings and doesn't want to harm the dragon.

A good helmet is vital to stay safe! Stoick gives Hiccup a special helmet when he becomes top of the class in dragon training.

ON THE ATTACK!

As you'd expect with Gobber as the local blacksmith, the Vikings of Berk have some scary-looking weapons!

Astrid's double-edged battle axe used to belong to her mother and, judging by its condition, it looks as though it had a lot of use! When Astrid's not using the axe, she's busy sharpening the blades.

Hiccup designed and built the Bola launcher in his workshop. He calls it the Mangler and its main function is to shoot down dragons from the sky. This is the weapon Hiccup uses to shoot down Toothless during a dragon raid.

Stoick's preferred weapon is his mighty hammer but he doesn't always need a weapon to defeat dragons. This Viking warrior is so strong that he fought off a Monstrous Nightmare with his bare hands!

Typical Viking Weapons

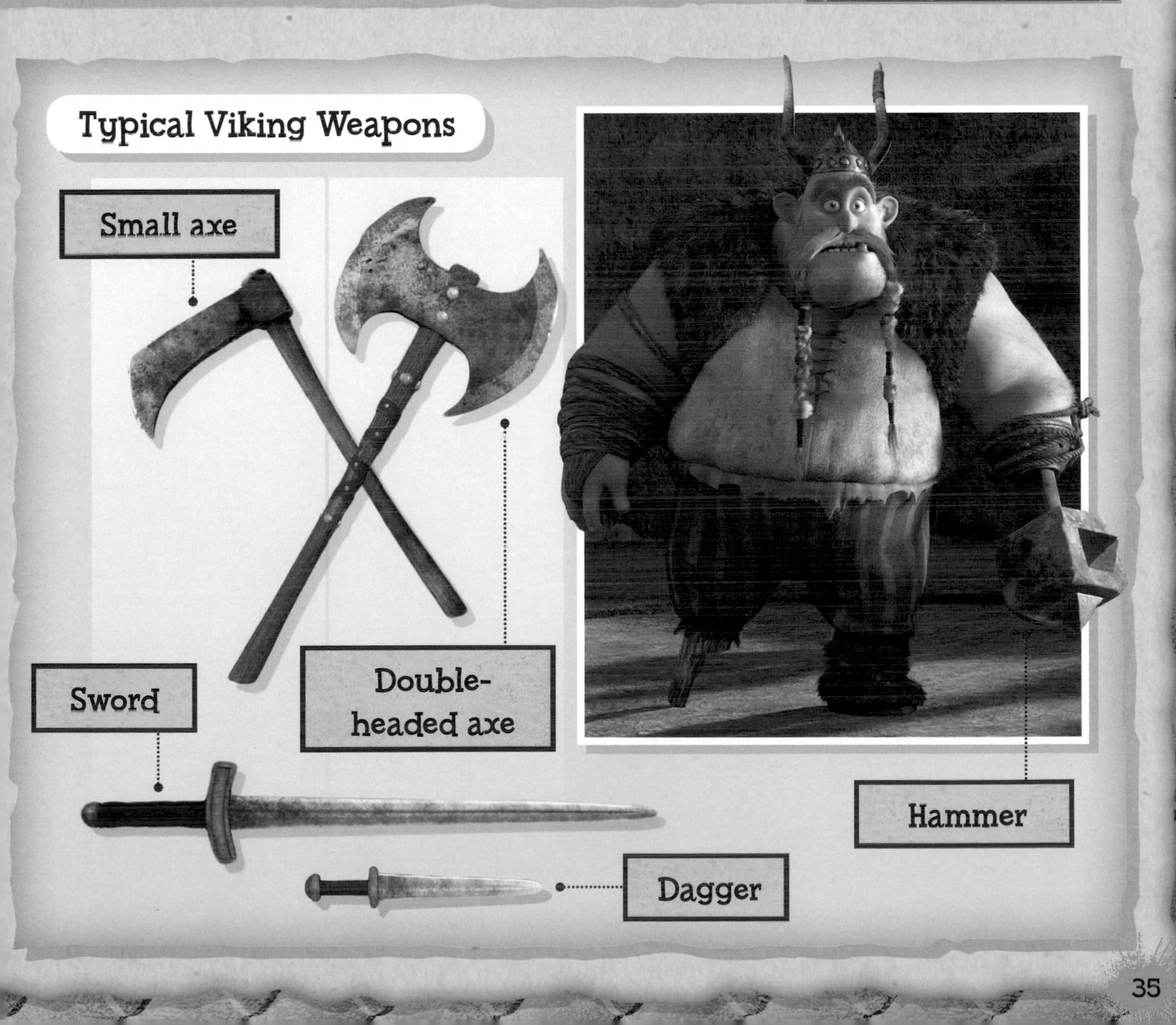

BACK TO BERK!

Five years have passed since the Vikings of Berk made peace with the dragons of the land, so it's definitely time to catch up with the Dragon Riders and find out what they've been getting up to!

We are the voice of peace. And bit by bit, we will change this world.

The Vikings have made the most of their newfound friendship with the dragons and now have a brand new sport called Dragon Racing! The Dragon Riders compete by flying on their dragons and catching sheep to earn points. The white sheep are worth one point and the black sheep is worth 10 points.

Their relationship may have gotten off to a rocky start but Astrid and Hiccup soon became great friends. Now, romance has blossomed for the young Vikings.

Hiccup and Toothless have been exploring new lands together. It turns out there's a lot to see beyond Berk!

Are you ready to relive the second incredible adventure with the Vikings of Berk?

These days, Berk is a very different, and more peaceful, place to live. Up until five years ago, battling dragons was all the Vikings knew. But thanks to Hiccup, the island is now at peace with the dragons and it's a much happier place to live.

Living side-by-side with the dragons means they can enjoy their new hobby – Dragon Racing! Besides being lots of fun, the competitive sport also brings the whole village together.

One day, during a Dragon Race, Stoick notices that his son is missing. Hiccup has gone off on an adventure with his dragon, Toothless. Now that he can ride freely, Hiccup has discovered there's a whole world to explore and he doesn't want to waste a moment.

After winning the race (of course!), Astrid and her dragon Stormfly go in search of Hiccup. She wants to know why he wasn't at the race. Hiccup explains that he's avoiding his father because he wants to make him the new Chief of Berk!

To cheer up Hiccup, Astrid suggests they explore further. They pass over a new land covered in ice. Suddenly a Dragon Trapper captures Stormfly in a net and chains her on his ship. Astrid and Hiccup rush to save her.

Eret, the Dragon Trapper, tells Hiccup and Astrid he works for a powerful conqueror called Drago Bludvist, who is on a mission to build a dragon army. Hiccup and Astrid feel hopeless but Toothless manages to free Stormfly.

Hiccup and Astrid make a quick getaway, Eret warns them their dragons won't be safe for long ...

Back on Berk, Hiccup tells Stoick about Eret. As soon as Hiccup mentions the name 'Drago', Stoick's eyes fill with fear. To Hiccup's surprise, his father already knows Drago.

Stoick immediately tells the other Vikings to keep their dragons close and stop flying. Berk must prepare for war. This is just what Hiccup feared.

Hiccup tries to convince Stoick that war isn't the answer but it's no good. Stoick believes that the era of peace is over and locks Berk's gates to stop people leaving. It's not enough to stop Hiccup and Astrid though!

Together with Toothless and Stormfly, Hiccup and Astrid leave to try and convince Drago he is wrong. Before they can find him, Eret captures them. The other Vikings arrive to rescue them but Hiccup won't give up that easily. He is convinced he can persuade Drago that living in peace with dragons is the answer.

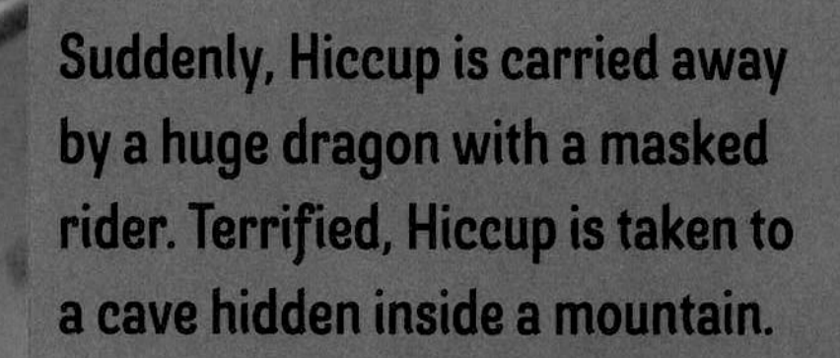

Suddenly, Hiccup is carried away by a huge dragon with a masked rider. Terrified, Hiccup is taken to a cave hidden inside a mountain.

When the dragon rider takes off the mask, she instantly recognises Hiccup as her son! Hiccup can't believe it! His mother, Valka, is alive and has been saving dragons all these years! Valka reveals they're standing in the home of the Bewilderbeast – the king of all dragons.

Meanwhile, Astrid, Stoick and the others are worried about Hiccup. They track him to the mountain and Stoick can't believe his eyes when he sees his long-lost wife!

As Stoick and Valka get reacquainted, they decide to return to Berk together. But before they can leave, Drago and his army attack the mountain!

Valka explains that Drago can never control the dragons, only the Alpha - the Bewilderbeast - is capable of that. But Drago has brought his own Bewilderbeast! It attacks Valka's dragon and wins, meaning all of the dragons bow down to their new Alpha - even Toothless!

Drago instructs Toothless to kill Hiccup and leaves to prepare for his invasion of Berk. Toothless, under the control of the new Alpha, fires a plasma blast at Hiccup but Stoick pushes him out of the way and is hit. Despite their best efforts to save him, Stoick is killed. Hiccup holds a Viking funeral for his father then vows to return to Berk and stop Drago.

Arriving back in Berk, the Vikings find that Drago has frozen everything and all the dragons are under the Bewilderbeast's control. Astrid, Valka and the Dragon Riders distract the Alpha while Hiccup confronts Drago.

The bond between Hiccup and Toothless breaks the Alpha's spell and together, they take on Drago and the Bewilderbeast.

The other dragons, seeing the bond between Hiccup and Toothless break out of their trance and join in the final fight. Together, the Dragon Riders and dragons defeat Drago and the Bewilderbeast, with Toothless firing the final blow. This act makes Toothless the new Alpha dragon!

Hiccup realises with Toothless by his side, he has nothing to fear and finally accepts his position as Chief of Berk in place of his father.

Whatever and whoever the Vikings of Berk face may well have armies or armadas ... but they have their dragons.

HICCUP AND TOOTHLESS

The heroic duo are back and a lot has changed since we first met them.

- Hiccup isn't so little these days - just look at how grown-up he is! He is more confident and has become the island's resident dragon expert.
- Hiccup and Toothless spend most of their free time exploring new and undiscovered lands. They're always on the lookout for new species of dragons, too.
- Hiccup and Astrid are now an official couple!

Thanks to all of his practice with Toothless, Hiccup has grown into a highly skilled flier.

- During Hiccup's battle with Drago, he is reunited with his long-lost mother, Valka. He hasn't seen her since he was a baby!
- Everyone on Berk thinks Hiccup is a hero for bringing peace between the dragons and Vikings of Berk.

- Night Furies used to be described as the 'unholy offspring of lightning and death itself', but Toothless has proven them wrong. He's playful, curious and will do anything to protect Hiccup.

- Toothless is the last known Night Fury and this makes him a target for Drago.

- Hiccup and Toothless defeat Drago's terrifying Alpha dragon, the Bewilderbeast. This makes Toothless the new Alpha!

- Toothless is loyal, brave and a natural leader. He's perfect for the role of Alpha dragon.

Astrid may be older and wiser but she's no less competitive!

- Astrid has become Dragon Race champion – the new sport of Dragon Racing was made for her!

Stormfly and Astrid train incredibly hard together before Dragon Races. Nothing can come between this dream team!

- Astrid is very intelligent and thinks fast under pressure. She never lets her emotions get in the way of making good decisions.

- Despite not always agreeing with him, Astrid admires Hiccup's bravery and the way he stands up for what he believes in.

FISHLEGS

Who could forget Berk's loveable dragon expert, Fishlegs? This brainbox knows every dragon fact and stat.

- Despite everything, Fishlegs still hates rule breaking. It makes him too nervous and he'd much rather play it safe.

- Fishlegs loves nothing more than researching dragon trivia with his dragon, Meatlug. He knows everything about all of the new dragons in Berk.

Large diameter bubbles, massive lungs, cold water deep dweller, I'm thinking class five leviathan, maybe six.

Fishlegs and Snotlout become rivals as they compete for Ruffnut's attention.

STOICK THE VAST

Stoick is getting used to life on Berk now that they live in peace with the dragons.

• Stoick is now the proudest father in Berk and he boasts about Hiccup whenever he can. It's quite a change from how he used to be!

• Stoick's job of protecting Berk is now much easier since they are not at war with the dragons. Stoick thinks it is time for him to step down as Chief and allow Hiccup to take the reins.

• When Stoick is reunited with his wife Valka, he can't believe his eyes. After she disappeared in a dragon raid when Hiccup was a baby, Stoick never heard from her again.

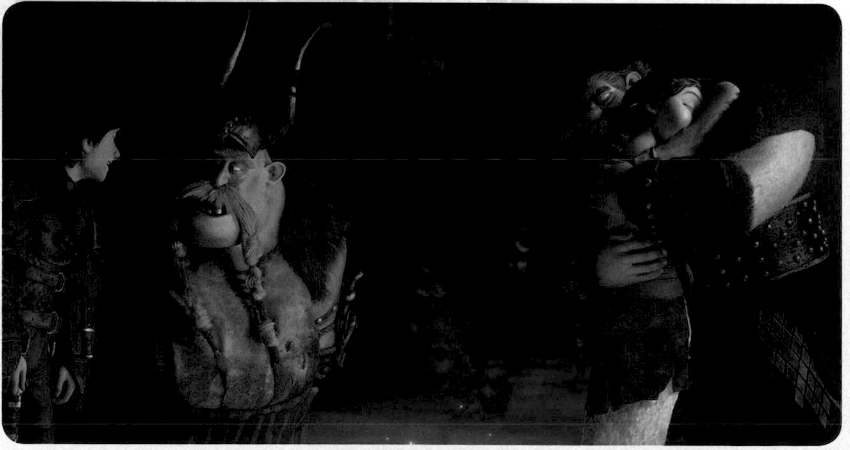

VALKA

Prepare to meet the strong, brave and determined Viking that is Valka!

- Twenty years ago Valka was abducted from Berk in a dragon raid. She has been living in the mountain cave ever since.

- Just as Hiccup did with Toothless, Valka spent time with dragons and learned their true ways. She believes that there should be peace between dragons and Vikings.

- Helping and protecting dragons has been Valka's life-long goal. She bravely puts her own life in danger to do so!

RUFFNUT AND TUFFNUT

Berk's bickering twins haven't changed much. They can still never seem to agree on anything, which is a bit tricky now that they share a two-headed dragon!

- Ruffnut is the strong-minded and danger-loving sister twin. She knows exactly what she wants in life and won't give up until she has it!

- Unlike Fishlegs, Ruffnut enjoys breaking rules wherever possible. It's more fun - and dangerous - that way!

- When Eret, son of Eret, comes into Ruffnut's life it looks as though there may be love in the air (if she has it her way!).

- Tuffnut is the thrill-seeking brother twin. He is totally fearless but he doesn't always act fast enough which can be a risky combination.

- In true twin style, this daring duo share a two-headed dragon called Barf and Belch. It's a Hideous Zippleback and, to add to their trouble, they don't always agree either!

SNOTLOUT

He's the Viking with the biggest ego you're likely to come across this side of ... anywhere!

- Snotlout thinks he's the most beautiful and popular Viking in town. One thing Snotlout doesn't have much of is modesty ...

- Snotlout's weapon of choice is a hammer. He doesn't need a fancy weapon when he has all the skill!

- No one has to wait too long to hear all about Snotlout and his strengths. He would talk about himself all day given the chance!

Snotlout and Hookfang work well together when they're competing against the other Dragon Riders. It's all about winning for this competitive team.

GOBBER

Stoick's right-hand man and Berk's trusty blacksmith, Gobber is always there to give advice to the young Dragon Riders.

• Gobber has an opinion about everything and he never holds back from sharing it.

• Grump is Gobber's fussy dragon. He's a drowsy Hotburple who can fall asleep if he's eating, flying or doing almost anything!

• Before the era of peace, Gobber made weapons to fight the dragons. Now he makes saddles for Dragon Racing and contraptions to make living with the dragons easier.

• Behind the tough exterior and blunt opinions, Gobber is very kind and loyal to his friends.

ERET
SON OF ERET

If it's a dragon trapper you're after then look no further than Eret.

- Eret's job is to provide a steady stream of dragons to a very tough customer ... Drago!

Eret has an inflated ego – he'd even give Snotlout a run for his money! He calls himself the 'greatest dragon trapper alive'.

- Drago's fiery temper is well-known so Eret spends his life trying to stay on the right side of him. He'd do anything to save his own skin.

- Eret's rugged looks catch the eye of none other than Ruffnut!

- Despite helping Drago initially, Eret ultimately realises the error of his ways and helps the Dragon Riders defeat Drago and the Bewilderbeast.

DRAGO BLUDVIST

Drago is a dragon trapper with a difference – he will stop at nothing to capture his prey.

- It's not just Drago's enormous size that's scary. He's also totally intolerant of anyone with a different opinion to him.

- Drago is a force to be reckoned with. Only the bravest or stupidest Vikings would ever willingly cross his path – even Stoick is fearful of him!

- Drago is on a mission to capture and control all the dragons in the world. He gave himself the title of 'Dragon God' and is determined to live up to the name.

- Drago will stop at nothing to carry out his plans. He thinks war is the answer and is a military genius.

STORMCUTTER

SPECIES: Stormcutter

CLASS: Sharp

SIZE: 31 feet 3 1/4 inches

WINGSPAN: 48 feet

HABITAT: Mountain cave

SKILLS: Can brake in mid-air, excellent sky divers

- Valka befriends a Stormcutter in the mountain and names it Cloudjumper.

- Stormcutters can navigate through tight spaces.

- Stormcutters are large and intelligent dragons. Cloudjumper is so in tune with Valka, she doesn't need a saddle. She can stand balanced on his back!

- Like an owl, Stormcutters can turn their heads almost all the way around - there's no hiding from a Stormcutter!

- Stormcutters can rest upside down, this gives them a unique view on the world below!

HOTBURPLE

SPECIES: Hotburple

CLASS: Boulder

SIZE: 14 feet

WINGSPAN: 18 feet

HABITAT: Caves

SKILLS: Shooting bursts of lava from iron ore they eat, immense jaw strength

• Hotburples live on a diet of rocks and iron ore.

• Hotburples have a bulbous tail that can be used like a mace in battle.

• When it comes to battle these dragons will always give it their all, that's why Gobber and his Hotburple, Grump, make such a good team.

RUMBLEHORN

- Rumblehorns can shoot long-range fire missiles from their mouth.

- They have clubbed tails and armoured necks and look a bit like a pig crossed with a rhino - only bigger!

- Rumblehorns often keep their battle axe-shaped muzzles in the dirt, sniffing things out.

- Stoick has a Rumblehorn that he rides called Skullcrusher.

SPECIES: Rumblehorn

CLASS: Tracker

SIZE: 11 feet 1/2 inch

WINGSPAN: 30 feet

HABITAT: Woods

SKILLS: Powerful sense of smell - can follow the faintest scent anywhere

VALKA'S BEWILDERBEAST

SPECIES: Bewilderbeast

CLASS: Tidal

SIZE: 520 feet

SKILLS: Despite their gargantuan size, they are incredibly fast swimmers; ice blasts

- Bewilderbeasts are the largest species of dragon known to the Vikings of Berk, even bigger than the Red Death.

- Valka found the Bewilderbeast in the mountain and she has lived there ever since. The creature has worked with Valka to rescue other dragons in danger.

- Drago orders his Bewilderbeast to fight Valka's so he can gain control of the dragons.

- After winning the fight and becoming the only Alpha, Drago uses the Bewilderbeast to command all of the dragons to leave with him. Now he has his dragon army!

- Bewilderbeasts are the only dragons who blast ice instead of fire.

SPECIES: Bewilderbeast

CLASS: 10 Levithian

SIZE: 520 feet

SKILLS: Can dominate and control the thoughts of dragons around it, forcing them to do what it commands.

DRAGONS OF THE MOUNTAIN SANCTUARY

Let's meet some other dragons from the mountain!

Species: Scuttleclaw
Size: 18 feet
Wingspan: 20 feet

Scuttleclaws are wild, hyperactive adolescent dragons. They are difficult to control and fly but are immune to the Alpha control of the Bewilderbeast so are very useful useful at helping the Dragon Riders fly back to Berk when Toothless is under control of Drago's Alpha.

Species: Hobblegrunt
Size: 55 feet
Wingspan: 63 feet

Not only is he sensitive to shifts in the moods of the dragons around him but, thanks to Valka's tutelage, Gruff can now subtly affect those dragons' emotional states. By altering his coloration and vibrating his crown, Gruff can send out a soothing signal to calm irritated dragons or whip them into action during an attack!

DRAGON SANCTUARY

Valka has lived in the Bewilderbeast's dragon sanctuary for the past twenty years.

When Valka was abducted from Berk, she made the mountain her home. She helped the sanctuary to flourish and took care of the dragons she has rescued from trappers over the years.

The mountain is home to the king of dragons, also known as the Bewilderbeast. All other dragons in the land bow to this Alpha dragon!

The mountain is based in an active volcanic region and is filled with hot springs. The climate is warm and moist – an ideal climate for a dragon's nest!

The mountainous area is made up of caves, waterfalls and cliffs, and there is also a large pool of seawater where the Bewilderbeast lives.

Valka has made a home for herself in a cavern. This is where she is reunited with Hiccup and Stoick!

THE FINAL CHAPTER!

Since we last saw Hiccup and the Vikings of Berk a lot has changed. Hiccup is Chief and the island is getting a little bit crowded ...

DreamWorks

HOW TO TRAIN YOUR DRAGON THE HIDDEN WORLD

In the thrilling finale to the trilogy, Hiccup and Toothless' bond is put to the test.

Hiccup and his dragon, Toothless, landed on the deck of a trapper ship. It was full of cages - and each one had a dragon inside it!

"I'm going to get you out of here," Hiccup promised the dragons.

"Attack!" cried the trappers.

Swinging his Dragon Blade, Hiccup fought the trappers and freed the dragons. Then he and Toothless soared into the air, leading the dragons to safety.

Back in the village of Berk, the streets teemed with dragons - from baby Gronckles to a giant Goregutter.

"You need to stop bringing dragons back here," Gobber told Hiccup. "It's too crowded."

Hiccup was proud of Berk, where dragons and people

lived together in peace.
"The trappers are closing in on us," Gobber warned Hiccup.
But Hiccup wasn't worried. "We can handle them," he boasted. "After all, we have the Alpha."
Toothless was the last remaining Night Fury and the most powerful type of dragon. All the other dragons followed him.

The trappers were furious that they'd lost the dragons. To get revenge they made a deal with a dragon hunter named Grimmel, who promised to capture the Night Fury. He set a trap, using a beautiful white dragon with shimmering scales as bait. As soon as he saw the Light Fury, Toothless fell in love with her. But when Hiccup turned up, the white dragon flew away.

Grimmel's plan had failed, but he wasn't going to give up.

"Give me the Night Fury,"

Grimmel demanded, sneaking into Hiccup's house.
"Over my dead body," Hiccup replied defiantly.
"Have my dragon ready when I return, or I will destroy everything you love!" threatened Grimmel. Then he whistled and menacing Deathgripper dragons burst in, setting Hiccup's house on fire with their flaming acid!

The Vikings gathered in the Great Hall.
"We need to leave Berk," Hiccup told the others.
"Our enemies are closing in."
Some villagers wanted to stay and fight. But others agreed with Hiccup.
"Leaving is the only way to keep the dragons safe," said Valka.

Hiccup remembered a Hidden World his father had told him stories about long ago. "We have to disappear off the map. Take the dragons to a place where no one will find them," he told the villagers.
The entire village packed up their belongings.
The flock of dragons took flight above ships loaded with supplies. Leading the way, Hiccup and Toothless soared through the clouds, searching for a new home.

They landed on a beautiful island with sparkling waterfalls, lush forests and snowy mountains. Tired from their long journey, the villagers set up camp by the lakeshore. Everyone started planning their new homes.

"Hang on," said Hiccup. "We're not staying for good." The villagers grumbled. They didn't believe that the Hidden World actually existed.

"OK, we can stay for now," said Hiccup. "But Toothless and I are going to keep looking for the Hidden World."

That night, as Hiccup slept in his tent, the white dragon suddenly appeared outside. The Light Fury had followed them! In the moonlight, Toothless tried to impress the beautiful girl dragon. He flapped his wings and puffed out his chest. He even drew a picture of her in the sand.

But when the Light Fury noticed Hiccup watching, she flew away again. She didn't trust humans.

like celebrating. He was worried about Toothless.

"I don't trust that Light Fury,"

said Hiccup. "She's too wild."

"Relax," Gobber assured him.

"Toothless will be fine."

Suddenly, Valka flew down on Cloudjumper.

"We're being tracked!" she cried, hopping off her dragon's back.

Grimmel had followed them on his airship, with hundreds of ships full of dragon cages sailing behind him!

Toothless was heartbroken. Hiccup felt terrible about scaring his dragon's new friend away. Unpacking his tools, Hiccup made a new tail fin for Toothless so that he could fly by himself.

"Go get your girl," Hiccup said, attaching the tail fin to Toothless. Smiling, Toothless gave Hiccup a slobbery slurp then flew off on his own.

"Let's get the dragons out of here," said Astrid. "Split them up."

"No," said Hiccup. "We're going to capture Grimmel!" Hiccup and his friends flew to an old trapper's fort, planning to launch a surprise attack on Grimmel.

Toothless searched the skies for the Light Fury. Just when he had given up hope, she appeared. The two love-struck dragons flew off together. The Light Fury led Toothless to a column of mist, rising out of the sea. She beckoned Toothless to follow her and vanished into the sparkling mist with him. Back in New Berk, a bonfire blazed and a feast was in full swing. But Hiccup didn't feel

But Grimmel was waiting for them with his ferocious Deathgrippers. A net dropped down, trapping the Dragon Riders with the hissing dragons!

"You're nothing without your dragon,"

taunted Grimmel. He snapped his fingers and the Deathgrippers opened fire, blasting flaming acid at the prisoners.

Valka swung her staff, summoning Cloudjumper. The dragon dove down and grabbed the net in its claws.
"Quick!" shouted Valka. "Climb up!"

The Vikings clung to the net as Cloudjumper flew up. Valka slashed a hole in the ropes with her staff. Hiccup and the others fell through the hole, plummeting through the air.

SWOOSH! Dragons swooped down to catch them just in time, flying them back to safety.

When they arrived back in New Berk, Toothless still hadn't returned.
"This is all my fault," said Hiccup, shaking his head sadly. "I shouldn't have let him go."
"Get on," said Astrid, patting Stormfly's saddle. "We're going to find Toothless."

Following her nose, Stormfly flew over the seas. At last she reached the column of mist and dived down into it. When the mist cleared, Astrid and Hiccup found themselves in a crystal cavern at the bottom of a waterfall - the Hidden World!

Thousands of dragons bowed down in homage to Toothless and the Light Fury. The dragons spotted the humans and roared, ready to attack.

"Stop!" commanded Toothless with a roar. The dragons obeyed their leader and backed down.
Toothless and Stormfly flew Hiccup and Astrid back home. To Toothless's delight, the Light Fury had followed them! Toothless proudly showed his mate around the island. But the Light Fury wasn't the only one who had tracked them to New Berk . . .

"Surprise!" said Grimmel, firing a dart at the Light Fury. Toothless bellowed and unleashed a fireball but - WHOOSH! - a second dart hit him in the side. The mighty Night Fury slumped to the ground, tame as a kitten. The darts were tipped with Deathgripper venom. Now both dragons were under Grimmel's control!

"Toothless!" Hiccup cried in dismay as Grimmel chained the groggy dragons to his airship and flew off with them. He watched helplessly as the other dragons flew after the airship, loyally following Toothless, the Alpha.

"Suit up!" ordered Hiccup. "We're going to get them back!"

Spreading the wings of their Dragon Armour, Hiccup and his friends glided towards the ships. Hiccup and Astrid attacked Grimmel's airship as the others freed dragons from the ships below.

"Take that!" shouted Hiccup, swinging his Dragon Blade.

Astrid bravely fought off soldiers with her axe.
Grimmel's Deathgrippers spat flames while Toothless blasted fireballs back at them. Soon the airship was ablaze!

"Go!" cried Grimmel, riding off on the Light Fury. Hiccup cut Toothless free and they took off in pursuit. Leaping off Toothless's back, Hiccup launched himself through the air at Grimmel, who fired a dart.

It hit Toothless, just as Hiccup knocked Grimmel off the Light Fury's back.

"Save Toothless," Hiccup told the Light Fury as they all plunged down to the sea.

Quick as a flash, the Light Fury rescued her unconscious mate, but then she came back for Hiccup.

SPLASH! Grimmel fell into the water but Hiccup was saved!

The Light Fury flew Hiccup back to New Berk, where the dragons and their rescuers had returned.

"You've looked after us long enough, bud,"

said Hiccup, giving Toothless a hug. He smiled at the Light Fury. "He's all yours." She and Toothless nuzzled each other happily.

Astrid removed Stormfly's saddle and lay her forehead on the dragon's horn. "I'll miss you, my good girl." One by one, the Vikings said goodbye to their dragons. As Hiccup watched proudly with tears in his eyes, the dragons flew to the Hidden World. There, they would finally be safe!

HICCUP AND TOOTHLESS

As the new Chief, Hiccup is in charge of all island decisions. Not an easy task when you're dealing with Vikings!

- Hiccup and his friends spend their time rescuing dragons from dragon trappers. They bring the dragons back to live safely on Berk.

- When a dragon hunter named Grimmel is after Toothless, Hiccup makes the difficult decision to leave Berk in search of the Hidden World.

- Hiccup makes a new tail fin for Toothless so he can fly by himself again. It's difficult for Hiccup to let him go, but he knows that it's time.

Hiccup and Toothless are still the same great friends – they make a formidable team!

- Toothless is now the Alpha dragon which means he commands all other dragons.

- Toothless is the only Night Fury in existence which makes him a target for dragon hunters like Grimmel.

It's love at first sight for Toothless when he sees the Light Fury in the woods. He does all that he can to impress her ... but it doesn't go quite to plan in the beginning!

ASTRID

Astrid often leads the charge on raids to rescue trapped dragons. She has become a strong and confident Viking.

- Astrid gives Hiccup advice and support about decision-making in Berk. They don't always agree but she will always support him.

- Astrid is more practical than Hiccup and can sometimes get frustrated when he won't accept change.

• When Toothless disappears with the Light Fury, Astrid tries to help Hiccup understand that maybe it's time to let Toothless live his own life.

Astrid and Hiccup first discover the Hidden World when searching for Toothless. Astrid can't believe it actually exists!

FISHLEGS

Fishlegs is still the go-to guy for dragon facts and stats.

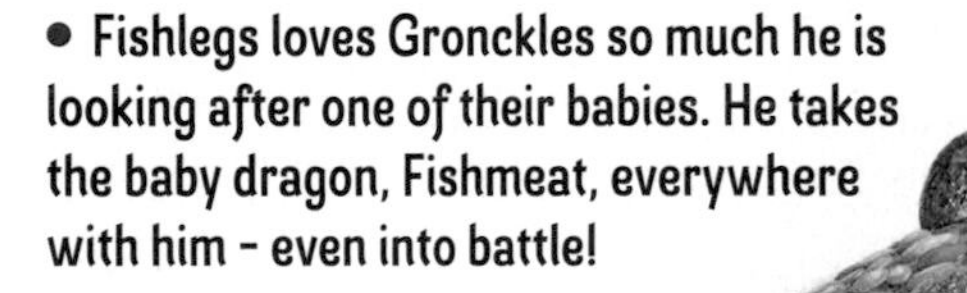

- Fishlegs loves Gronckles so much he is looking after one of their babies. He takes the baby dragon, Fishmeat, everywhere with him - even into battle!

- Despite being reluctant to break the rules or get in trouble, Fishlegs won't give up on his friends when it comes down to it.

- When Toothless discovers the Light Fury, Fishlegs is keen to add the information to his collection of dragon cards.

SNOTLOUT

Still as arrogant as ever, Snotlout has taken to the new way of life on Berk. He thinks he is the best at saving dragons, of course!

- Snotlout is infatuated with Valka. He thinks they would make the perfect couple but Valka isn't so sure!

- Despite some of the comments Snotlout makes, he trusts Hiccup and is willing to follow him in his search for the Hidden World.

RUFFNUT AND TUFFNUT

The twins haven't changed a lot - they still argue as much as ever!

- When Ruffnut is captured by Grimmel she talks so much that she drives Grimmel and the other trappers crazy!
- Ruffnut accidentally lets slip the location of Hiccup and Toothless so Grimmel sets her free and follows her.
- Ruffnut is still interested in Eret - and she makes sure he doesn't forget it!

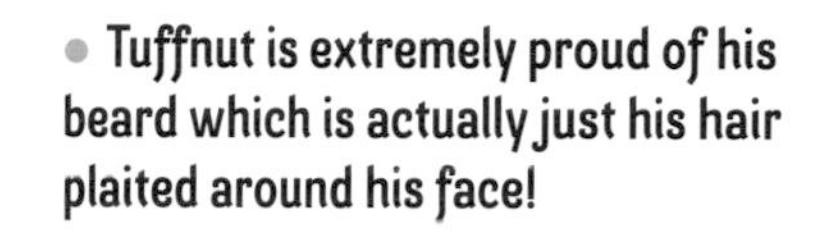

- Tuffnut is extremely proud of his beard which is actually just his hair plaited around his face!

- Tuffnut takes it upon himself to give Hiccup advice on his relationship with Astrid. It includes telling him to lose his limp, to which Hiccup responds he has a prosthetic leg!

ERET

Eret is no longer a dragon trapper. He lives on Berk with the rest of the Vikings and helps them to free dragons.

- Eret is a big and intimidating Viking. He is a good friend to have when it comes to battles!

- Grimmel knows Eret from his dragon trapping days and is surprised to see him with Hiccup and the rest of the Vikings from Berk.

- Despite Ruffnut's many attempts, Eret isn't interested in the talkative twin.

VALKA

Since reuniting with her son, Hiccup, Valka now lives on Berk.

- Valka discovers that Grimmel has been tracking the group and is on his way to New Berk along with an armada of ships and cages for all of the dragons.

- Valka is still fiercely passionate about protecting dragons and is delighted to now be part of a team who can help.

- Although difficult, Valka knows that it is time to let the dragons leave so they can be safe in the Hidden World. But that doesn't mean she won't miss her beloved Cloudjumper.

GRIMMEL AND THE DEATHGRIPPER

Grimmel is one of the most feared dragon hunters. He spends his time travelling the world searching for dragons.

Poison from Deathgrippers is deadly but in small quantities it is a powerful sedative. Grimmel uses this to subdue dragons he captures, including the Light Fury!

- Grimmel thought he had captured and killed every Night Fury in existence – that is until he saw Toothless! He makes it his mission to capture Toothless by any means ...

- Grimmel travels by airship. This special ship means he can quickly get to new locations – especially useful when you're chasing flying dragons!

SPECIES: Deathgripper

CLASS: Strike

SIZE: 28 feet

WINGSPAN: 32 feet

SKILLS: A venomous stinger that can kill or subdue other dragons

- Grimmel commands a number of terrifying Deathgrippers. Their tail is similar to a scorpion's and Grimmel uses their venom to control other dragons.

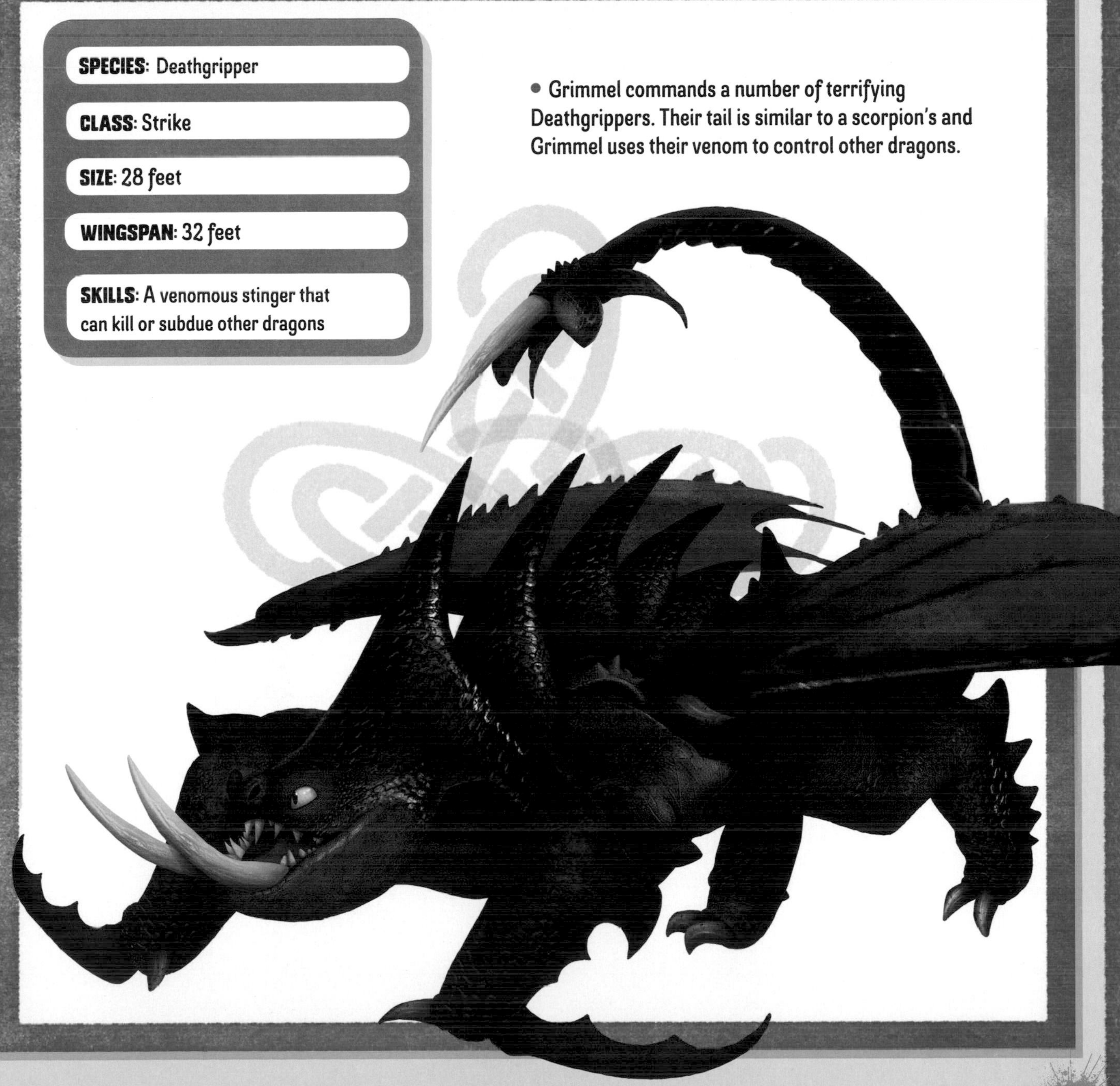

LIGHT FURY

Never before seen, the Light Fury is wary of humans, having been captured and contained in the past.

- The Light Fury can fly as fast as Toothless and blends easily into the daytime sky with her white coloration. The Light Fury can disappear into clouds, sea fog and the distant horizon.

- When Grimmel sees the Light Fury he immediately uses her as part of his plan to capture Toothless. He keeps her subdued with Deathgripper venom.

The Light Fury and Toothless may look like opposites but they have a special bond that is undeniable. Their connection creates a wonderfully balanced energy, much like yin and yang.

- It may be love at first sight for Toothless but the Light Fury isn't so sure! Toothless tries his best to impress her (even dancing!) and she quickly grows to love him.

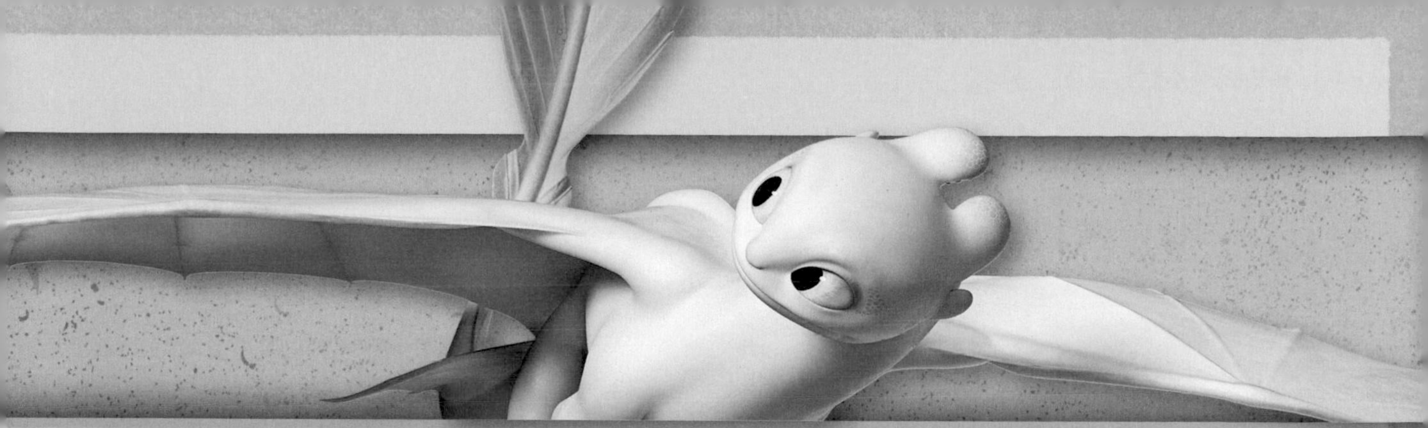

SPECIES: Light Fury

CLASS: Strike

SIZE: 22 feet

WINGSPAN: 42 feet

SKILLS: When she flies through the plasma blasts she emits, her scales become reflective for camouflage.

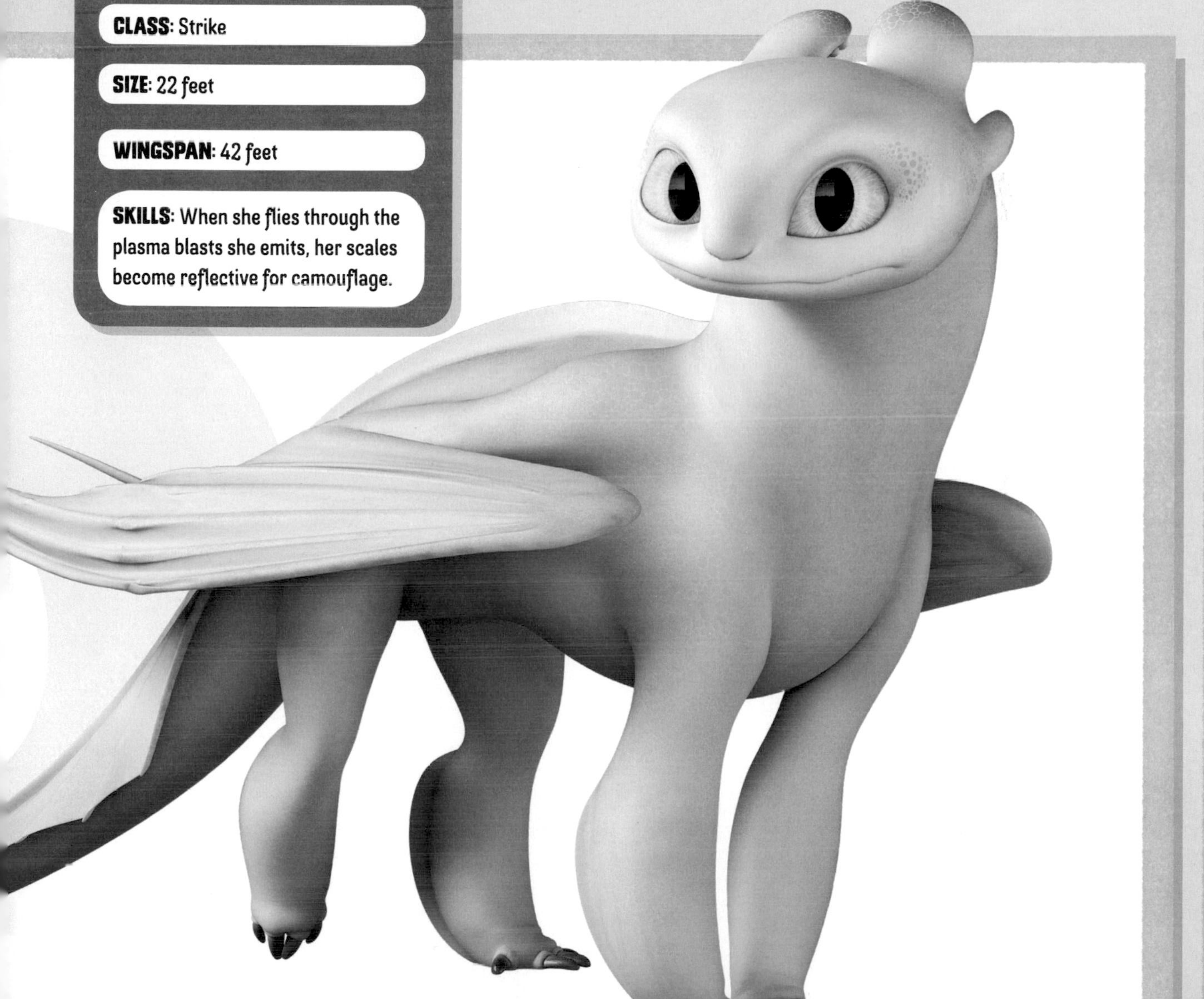

STORMFLY

- When Toothless goes missing, Stormfly flies Hiccup and Astrid to the Hidden World. Her tracking skills and strong sense of smell lead her there.

- Stormfly loves to preen her feather-like scales like a bird. But when it comes to battle, she's not worried about getting involved in the action!

SPECIES: Deadly Nadder

CLASS: Tracker

SIZE: 30 feet

WINGSPAN: 42 feet

SKILLS: Spine shots, magnesium fire blasts (the hottest of any dragon)

MEATLUG AND HOOKFANG

SPECIES: Gronckle

CLASS: Boulder

SIZE: 14 feet

WINGSPAN: 18 feet

SKILLS: Firepower is flaming chunks of rocks and lava

• Meatlug and Fishlegs have one of the strongest bonds between a dragon and rider. They do everything with one another. Meatlug accompanies Fishlegs while he's researching dragon trivia and she loves belly rubs and licking Fishlegs' feet. And naturally, they love flying together.

SPECIES: Monstrous Nightmare

CLASS: Stoker

SIZE: 61 feet

WINGSPAN: 68 feet

SKILLS: Igniting its whole body for self defence

• Hookfang and his rider Snotlout are very much alike - they are both arrogant and extremely stubborn! Hookfang loves nothing more than disobeying his rider but when it really matters, they make a great team.

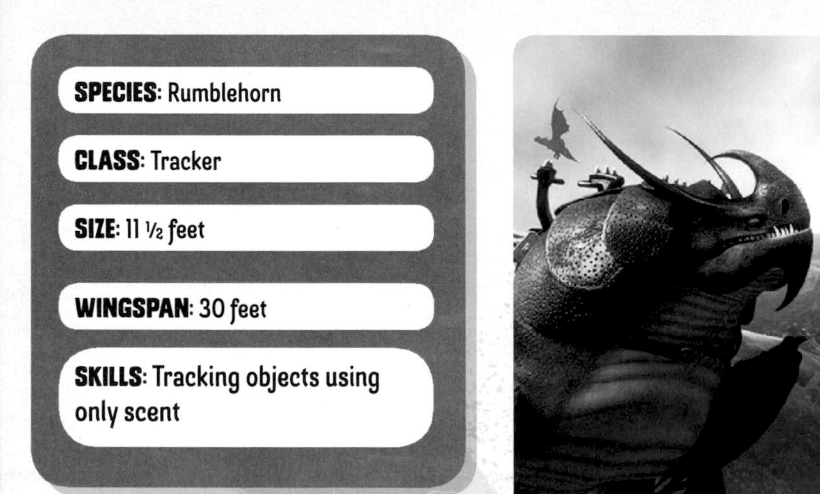

SPECIES: Rumblehorn

CLASS: Tracker

SIZE: 11 ½ feet

WINGSPAN: 30 feet

SKILLS: Tracking objects using only scent

• Skullcrusher was Stoick's dragon but now he partners with Eret. With Eret's former dragon trapping skills, they can track down anything in no time!

• Gobber often calls Grump "a large, snoring oaf of a dragon" (because he is!) but these two are the perfect pairing. Grump even keeps the flames going in Gobber's blacksmith shop.

SPECIES: Hotburple

CLASS: Boulder

SIZE: 14 feet

WINGSPAN: 18 feet

SKILLS: Bulbous tail can be used like a club

BARF AND BELCH AND CLOUDJUMPER

SPECIES: Hideous Zippleback

CLASS: Mystery

SIZE: 66 feet

WINGSPAN: 38 feet

SKILLS: Flaming wheel of death

- Just like Ruffnut and Tuffnut, Barf and Belch don't always get along. But when the two heads and their riders all work together, they are a force to be reckoned with!

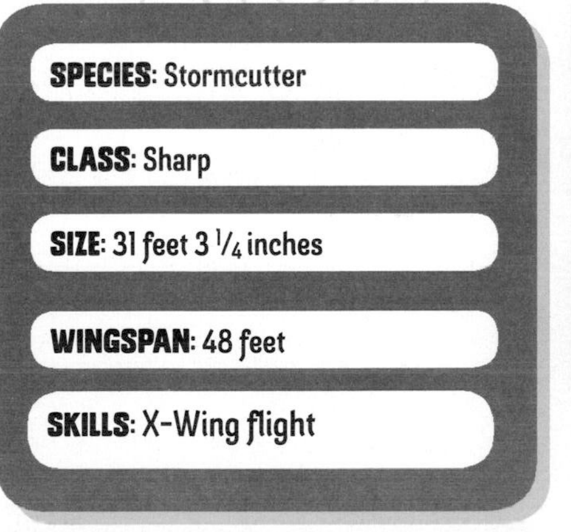

SPECIES: Stormcutter

CLASS: Sharp

SIZE: 31 feet 3 ¼ inches

WINGSPAN: 48 feet

SKILLS: X-Wing flight

- Valka was captured by a Stormcutter when Hiccup was young and taken to the dragon sanctuary. There Valka learned about dragons and ultimately lived with them in peace. She named the dragon who had taken her away Cloudjumper and they have a very strong bond.

THE HIDDEN WORLD

The Hidden World is home to all dragons and can only be found by a dragon – no humans could track it down alone.

Stoick had told Hiccup stories about the Hidden World when he was a child but everyone thought it was just a myth.

In the Hidden World, dragons glow brightly in the dark light and can live without fear of capture by dragon trappers.

EXPLORE FURTHER WITH HICCUP AND TOOTHLESS

DreamWorks

HOW TO TRAIN YOUR DRAGON

THE HIDDEN WORLD

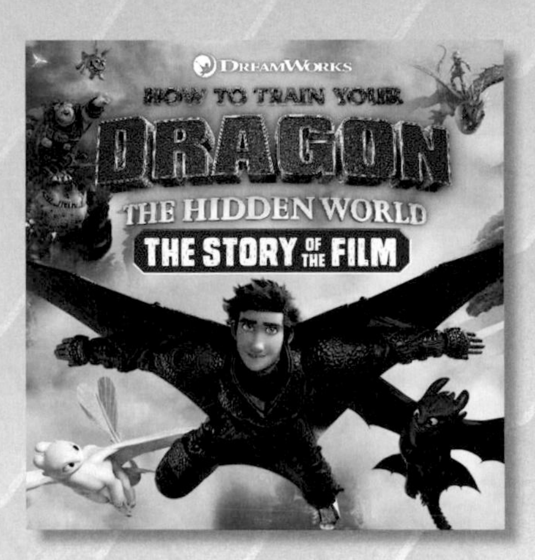